Where are THE BEATLES?

Find the iconic Fab Four

igloobooks

Where are THE BEATLES?

Can you find the Fab Four?

Once upon a time, there were four lads from Liverpool who became the ultimate pop band of the Sixties. They burst onto the scene and dramatically changed the face of music, fashion and the entire culture of the times for young, impressionable people. The Beatles, or the 'Fab Four', as they were also known, were quite simply legendary. We all know this, but whilst they must have mostly enjoyed their well-deserved fame, they must have occasionally found it tiresome to be followed around by persistent paparazzi, snooping journalists from radio and TV with their invasive questions plus, of course, the hordes of screaming fans!

How amazing would it have been if they could have escaped the gathering crowds to remain out of sight for a while?! These talented young musicians would have found it very difficult to remain anonymous and the scenarios illustrated in this quirky book show the sorts of places where they would have been found.

Could all four Beatles stay hidden in the confines of a jam-packed Yellow Submarine? Imagine that submarine gliding through the depths of the sea surrounded by psychedelic scenes of funky fish and discarded debris only to emerge just outside the Albert Docks in Liverpool! Ardent fans would be standing on the quayside waiting for their idols to disembark and the scene would be one of pandemonium! The Beatles would be spotted immediately… wouldn't they?

Whilst in Liverpool, The Beatles would have performed many times at the Cavern Club, which is where it all began! A tiny venue in the heart of the city, this place would have been throbbing both inside and out with enthusiastic followers of the band. It would have been challenging – to say the least – concealing four such famous faces!

From Liverpool, head down south for a visit to the famous Abbey Road studios. Here, the Fab Four would have walked across the equally famous zebra crossing many times. A busy London street, it would have been full of cars, traffic wardens and of course, the obligatory crowd of adoring fans who would have gathered in the hope that their favourite four might be spotted. Would these superstars have found anywhere to hide in that sort of situation?

Living a life in front of the cameras must get exhausting. Even The Beatles need some TLC from time to time… So how about a weekend at a yoga retreat in India? Imagine a beautiful, peaceful setting with mountains and crystal-clear waterfalls. But would the four lads be able to meditate without gaining unwanted attention from excitable yogi fans?

Picture the scene at JFK Airport, as the plane in which The Beatles' travel touches down onto the runway! Security guards would be in place to control the baying crowds as the excitement of The Beatles landing in the USA took hold.

But would it be a doddle to hide oneself while that kind of commotion ensued?

A Magical Mystery Tour would surely be the perfect scene in which to stay out of sight. Parked behind Penny Lane, the packed party bus would be rocking with folk inside and more outside, trying to get in! Where would John, Paul, George or Ringo have hidden amongst the subsequent kaleidoscopic chaos?!

Keep your eyes pinned, not only for The Fab Four, featured in each spread, but some easily identifiable items and celebs hidden throughout the intricately illustrated pages.

Good luck!

Yellow Submarine

758936140

758936140

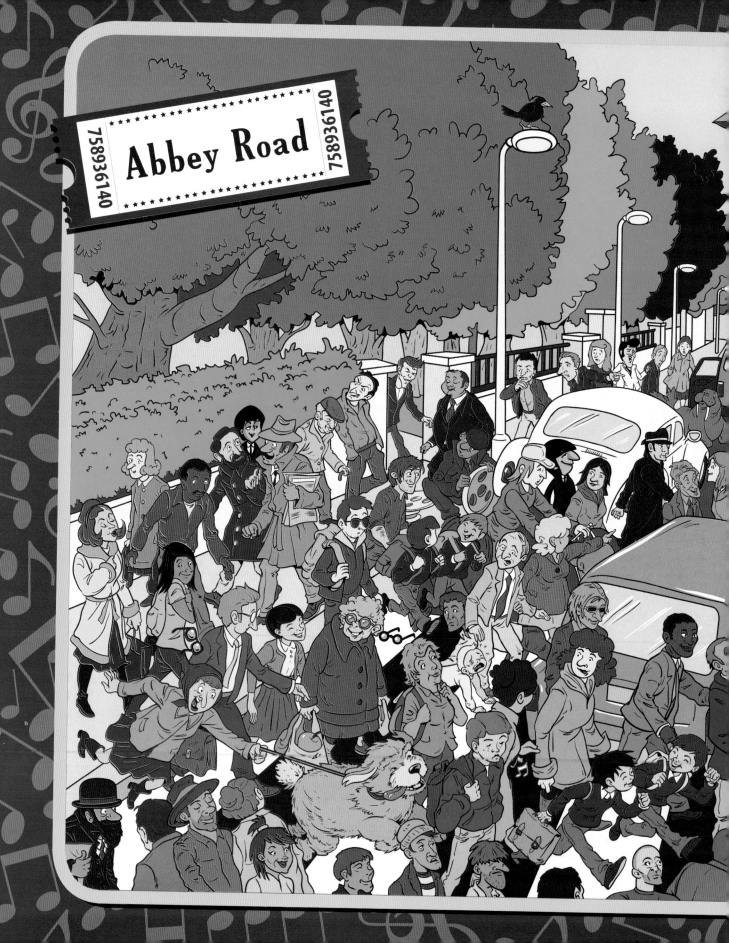

Indian Retreat

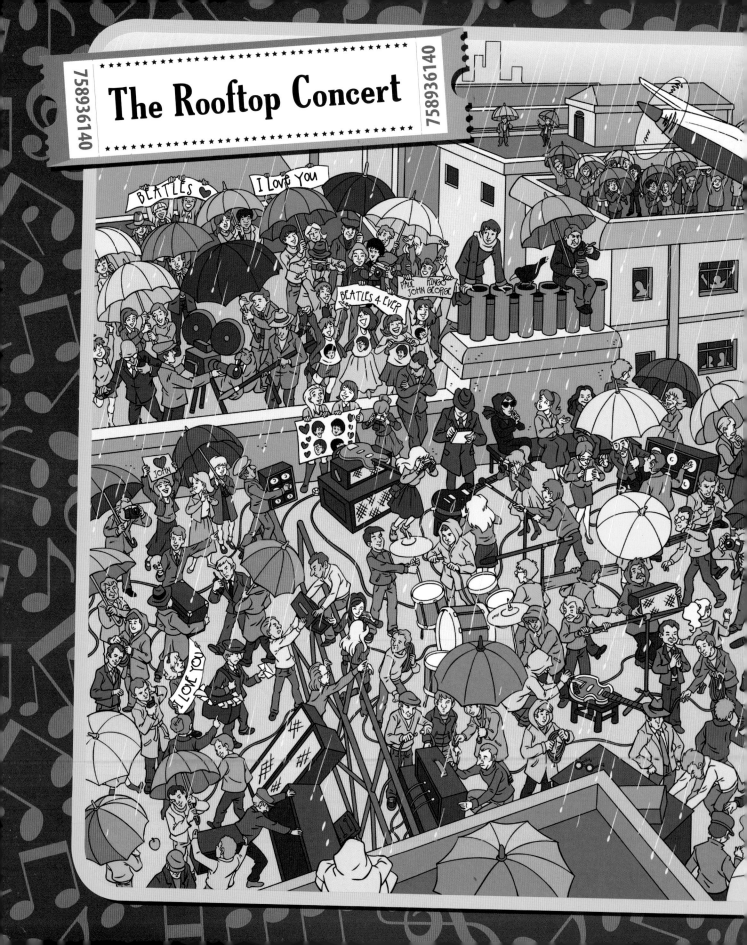

NEWSPAPERS

FLORIST

TICKETS

Hard Day's Night

758936140

758936140

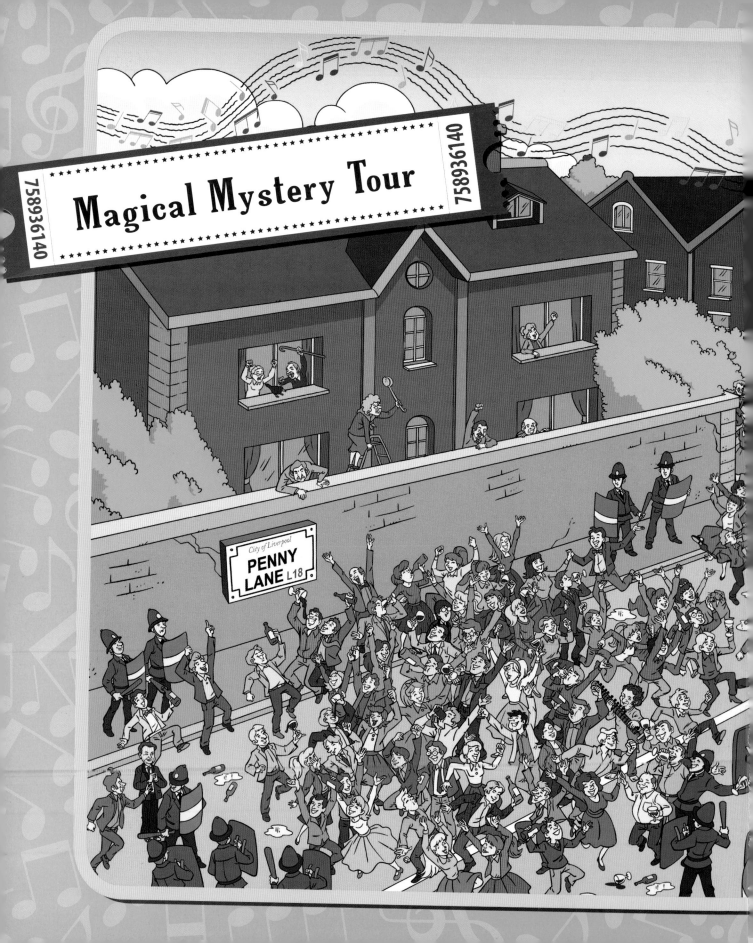

Elvis Presley –
A huge influence not only on the Fab Four, but the entire world of pop music. Elvis should be quite easy to spot among the wealth of other famous faces!

David Bowie –
It was Liz Taylor who introduced David Bowie to The Beatles. Years later Bowie classed John Lennon as 'probably his greatest mentor'.

Bob Dylan –
Allegedly, it was the American folk legend Bob Dylan who first introduced the band to marijuana when they met in NYC in 1964.

Pattie Boyd –
The English model and actress met George Harrison on the set of A Hard Day's Night in 1964 and they went on to marry two years' later.

Eric Clapton –
Clapton's band, The Yardbirds, supported The Beatles at a gig in London's Hammersmith. Ironically, he struck up a lasting friendship with George, whose ex-wife Pattie later became Mrs Clapton!

Linda McCartney –
A photographer, musician and animal rights activist, Linda met Paul McCartney in London in 1967. Wed in 1969, they remained together until her death in 1998.

Madonna –
Look out for the Material Girl, with the recognisably sassy style, who burst onto the pop scene in the early 80s, pushing the boundaries of lyrical and visual content as she went!

George Martin –
Sir George Martin CBE, affectionately known as the 'fifth Beatle', signed them to EMI and went on to be producer, arranger and mentor to the Fab Four.

Wilfrid Brambell –
Known for his role as the crotchety Alfred Steptoe in 'Steptoe and Son', Wilfrid also played Paul's grandad in the film 'A Hard Day's Night'.

The Maharishi –
The Beatles met the Indian Guru in 1967 and became fascinated by his techniques of transcendental meditation. They visited his spiritual training camp in India.

Yoko Ono –
A Japanese artist and musician, Yoko married John Lennon in March 1969 and was with him until his tragic death.

Brian Epstein –
Epstein, who also managed Gerry & the Pacemakers and Billy J Kramer & the Dakotas, became manager of The Beatles in 1962, and was key to their success.

Ravi Shankar –
Best known for popularizing the sitar and Indian classical music in the western world, Ravi Shankar's style influenced George Harrison in particular.